CONTENTS

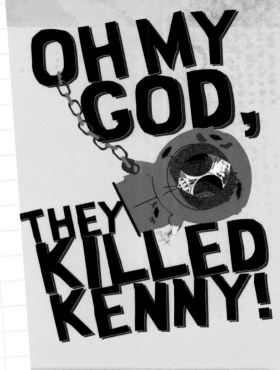

OH MY GOD, THEY KILLED KENNY!

Pedigree®

Published 2010. Pedigree Books Ltd, Beech Hill House, Walnut Gardens, Exeter, Devon EX4 4DH
books@pedigreegroup.co.uk | www.pedigreebooks.com

ERIC CARTMAN

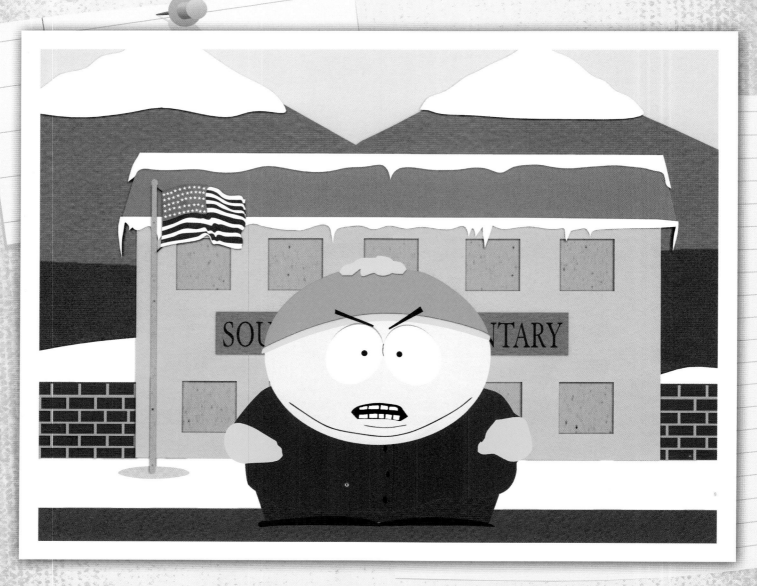

WHY DON'T YOU GO KNIT ME A SWEATER
BEFORE I SLAP YOU IN THE FACE!

KENNY McCORMICK

MPHRMPH.

KYLE BROFLOVSKI

YOU DON'T FART WHEN YOU'RE LOCKED IN A SMALL PLACE WITH OTHER PEOPLE!

STAN MARSH

DUDE, WHAT THE HELL IS WRONG WITH YOU?

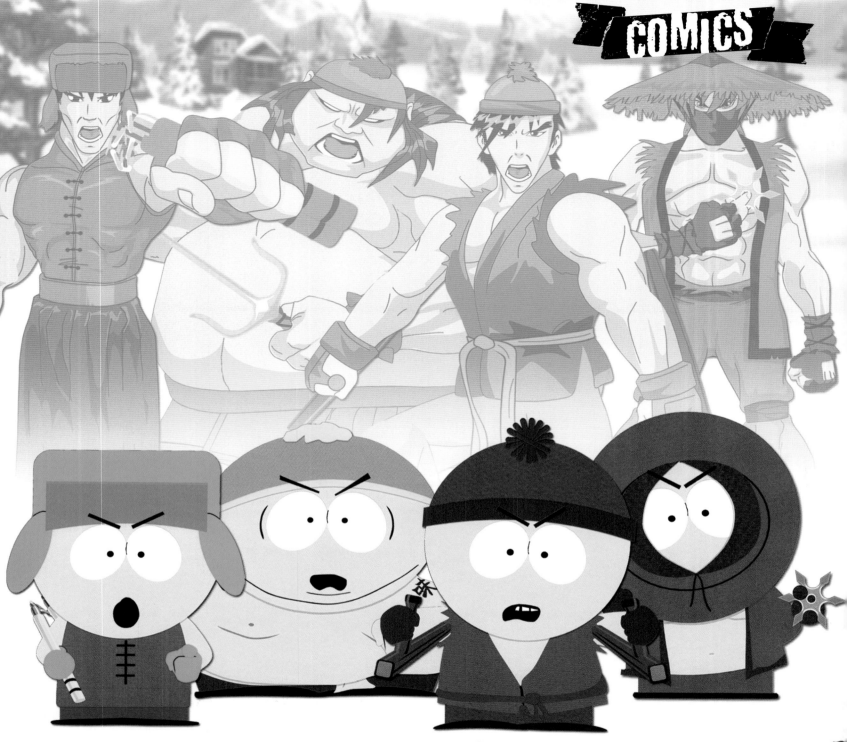

SOUTH PARK™

COMICS

GOOD TIMES WITH WEAPONS

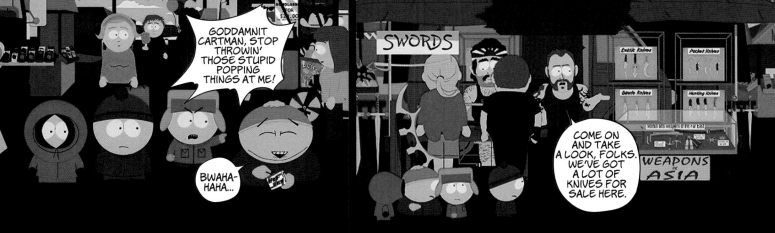

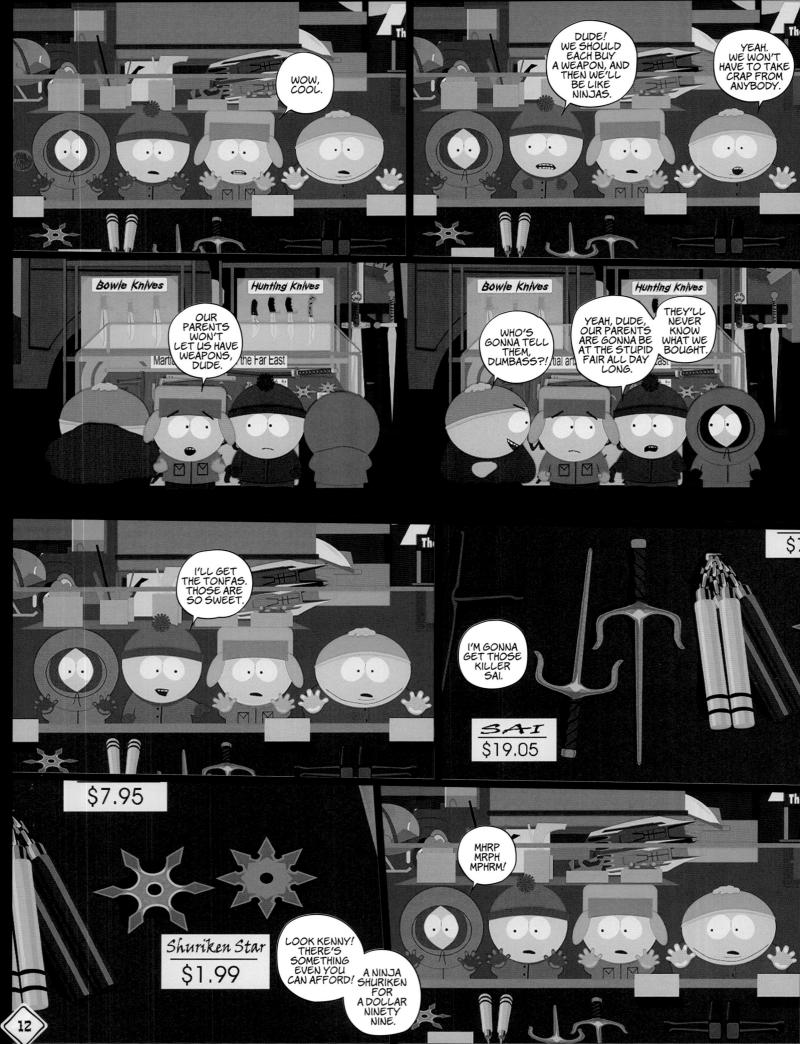

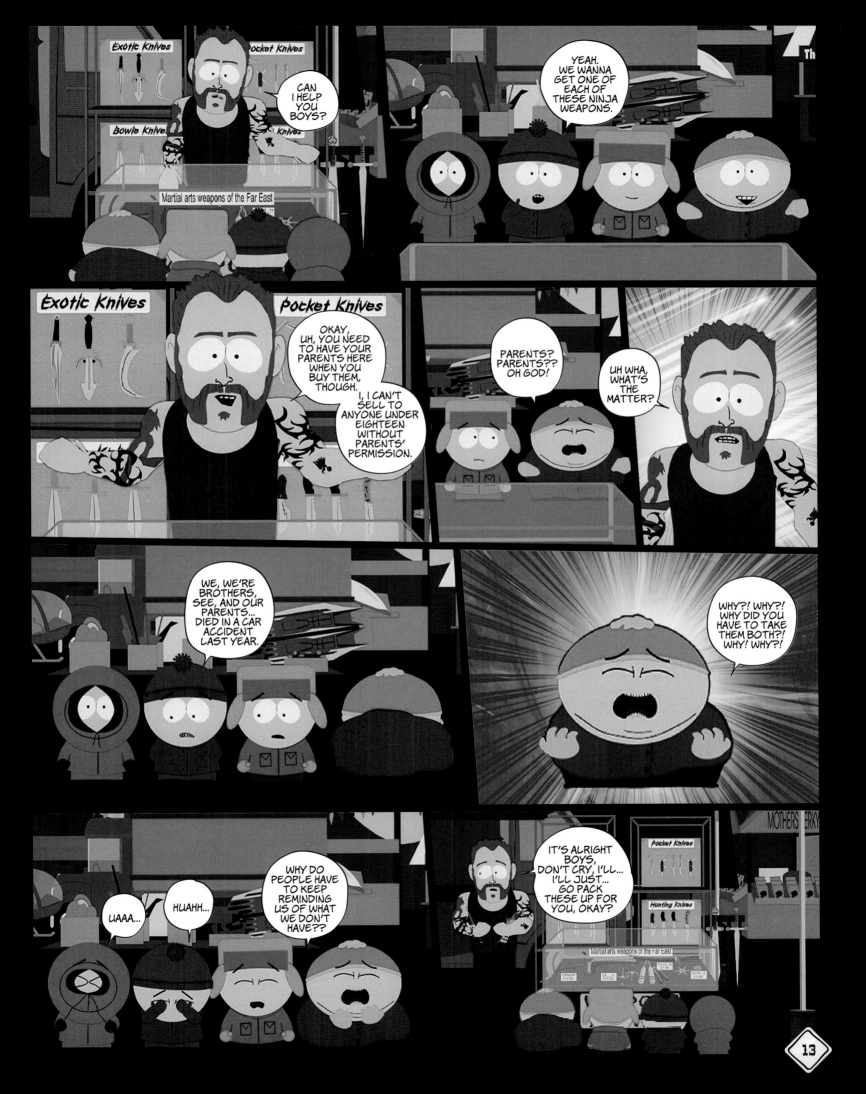

YES. I AM BULROG.
TOUGH BRUTE NINJA WHO HAS DEDICATED HIS LIFE TO ERADICATING THE WORLD OF HIPPIES.
BULROG!!
ALRIGHT, NINJAS! LET'S GO PROTECT THE WORLD!
KICK ASS!
HEY GUYS, YOU KNOW WHAT WE SHOULD DO?
WE SHOULD GO SHOW OUR WEAPONS TO CRAIG AND THOSE GUYS. THEY'LL BE SO JEALOUS.
HUHU... UHU...

WHOA! WHERE'D YOU GET THOSE??

YES. THE LIFE OF A NINJA IS COMPLEX AND FULL OF PERIL.

UH, WE'D LOVE TO HANG OUT GUYS, BUT WE HAVE IMPORTANT SECRET WORK TO DO.

COME ON, NINJAS! HO!

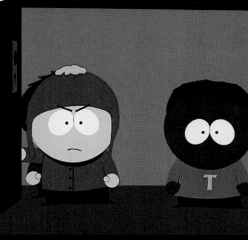

BAMMM!

OH MAN, DID YOU SEE THE LOOK ON CRAIG'S FACE?! THAT WAS AWESOME!

DUDE, WE'RE LIKE THE COOLEST KIDS IN THE WHOLE STATE!

SOCIETY CAST ME OUT, AND SO I VOWED TO MAKE THEM ALL PAY! AND PAY THEY DID!

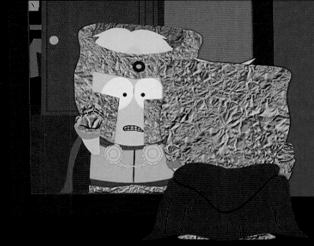

NOBODY KNOWS THAT BENEATH THIS SWEET EIGHT-YEAR-OLD LITTLE BOY LIES THE MOST EVIL.

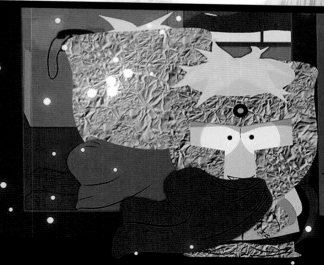

THE MOST DESTRUCTIVE SUPER VILLAIN OF ALL TIME!

WHOOOF

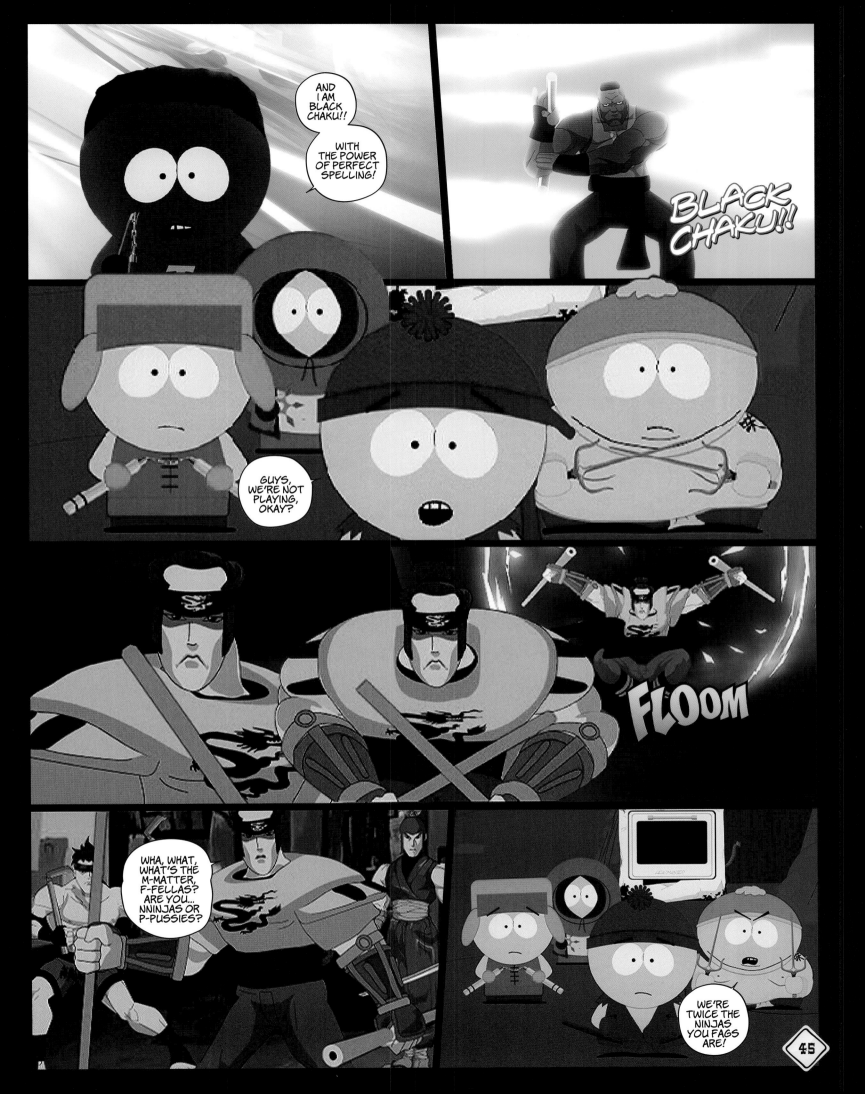

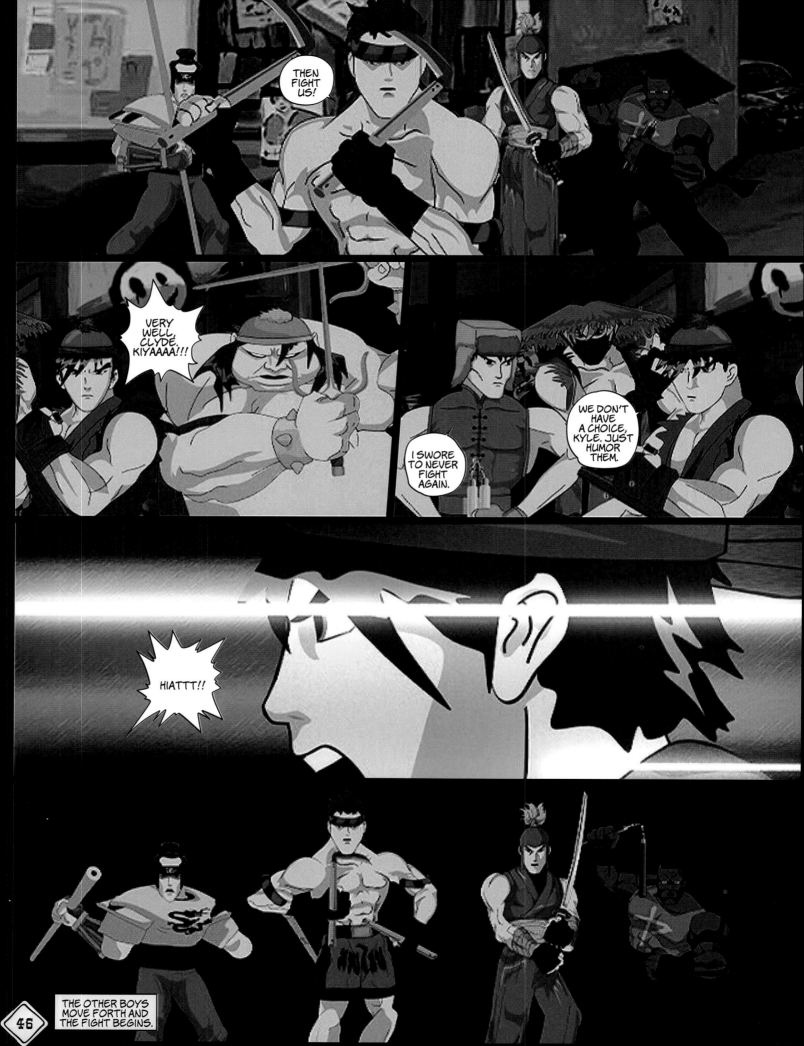

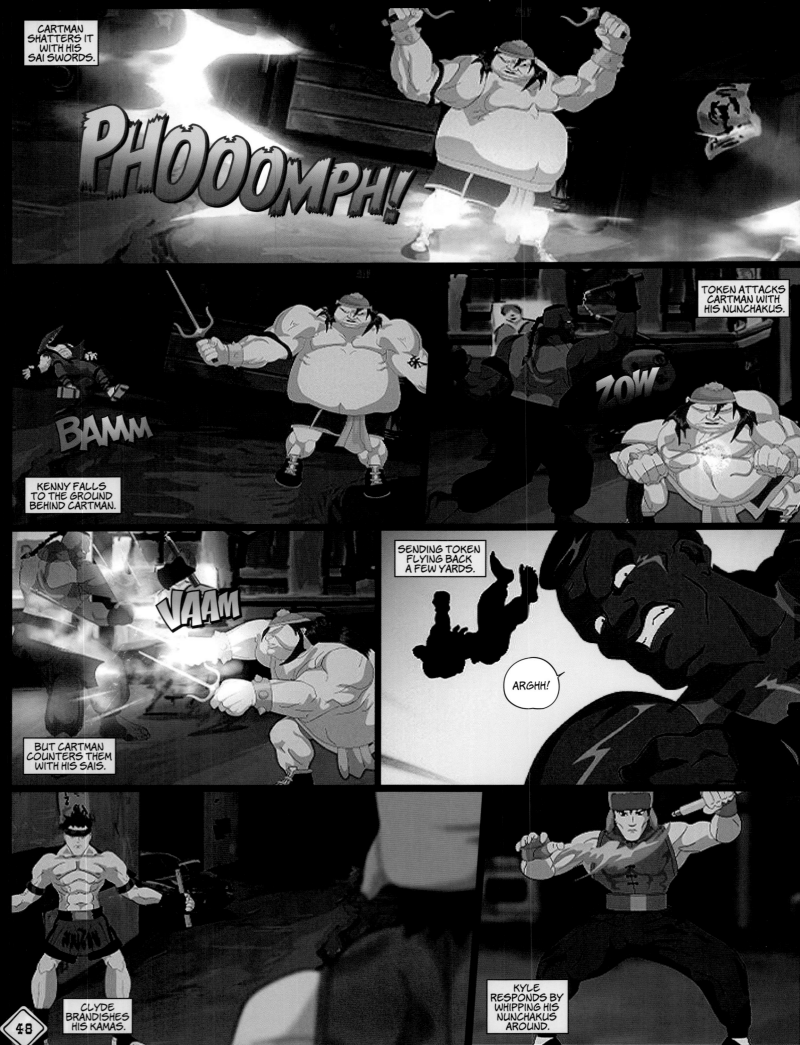

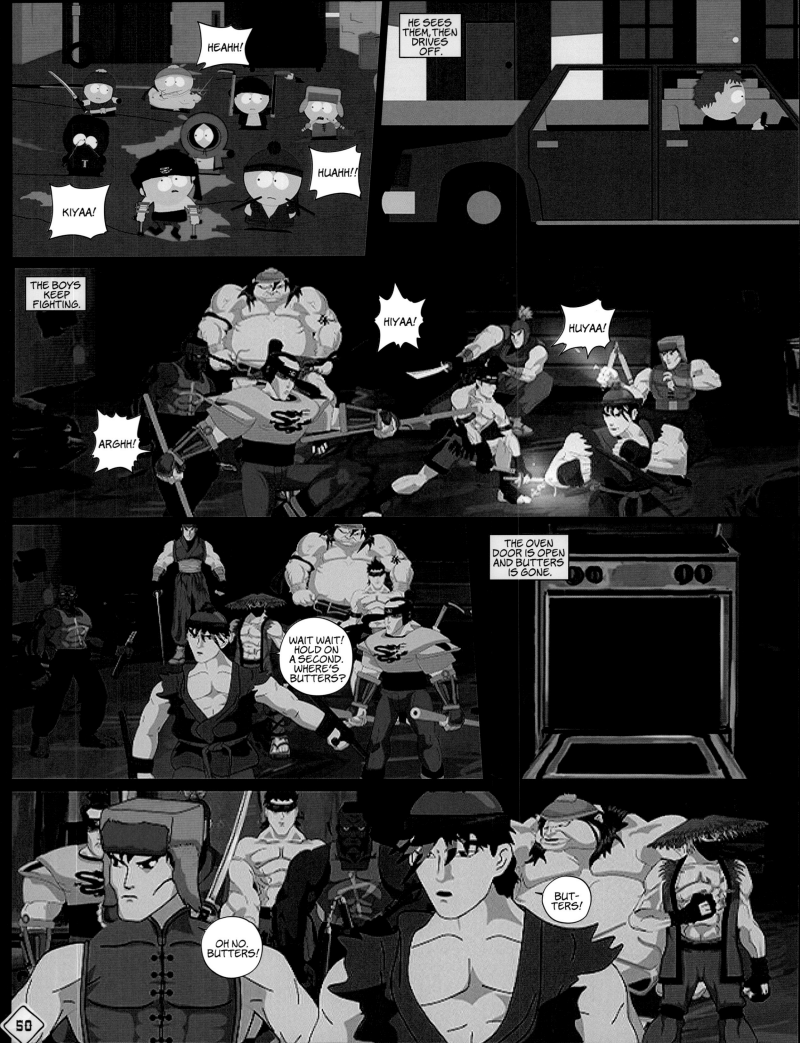

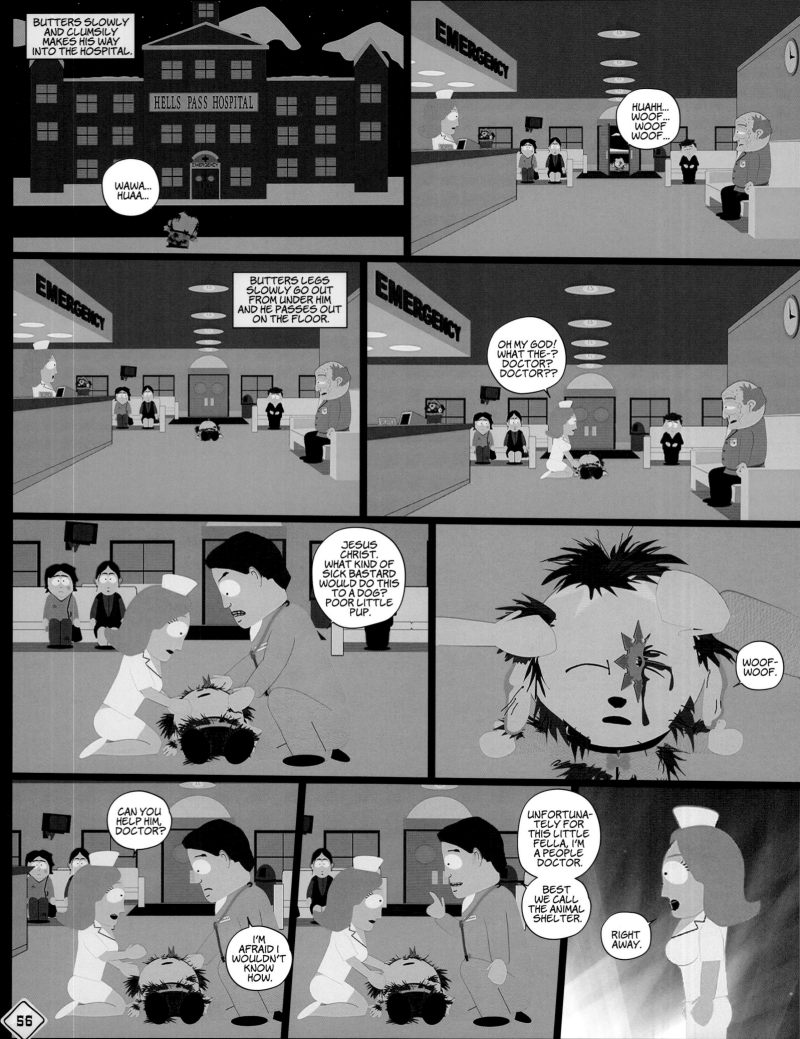

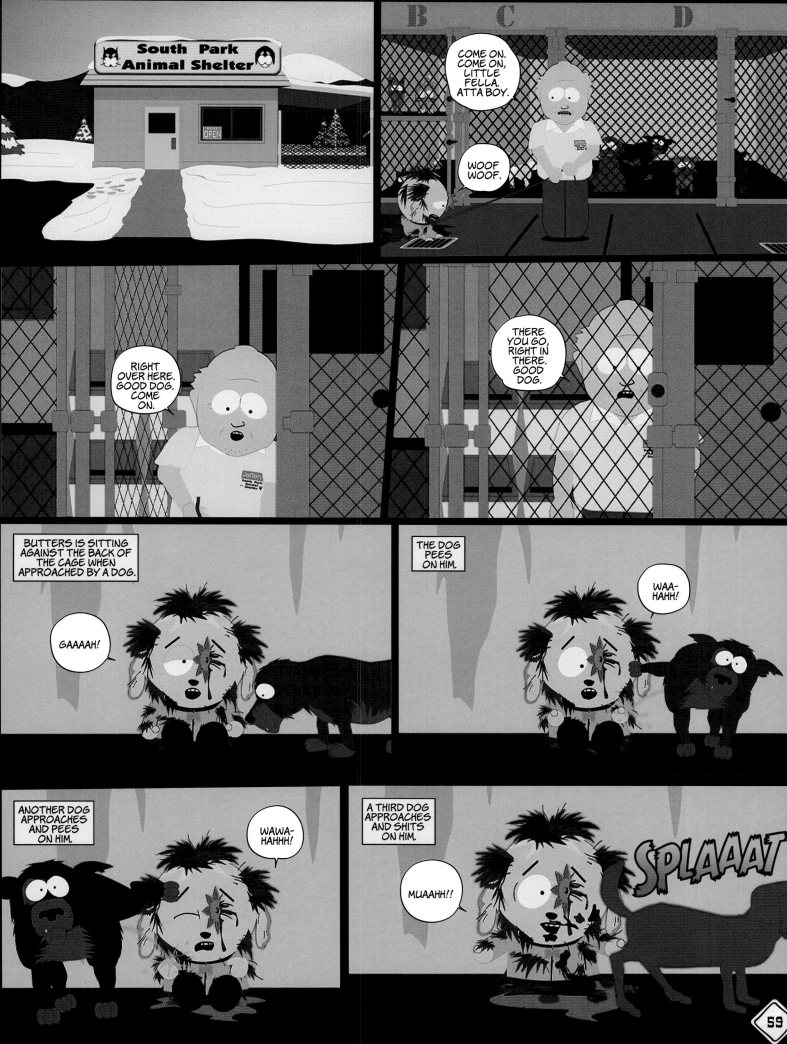

RIGHT ON THE OTHER SIDE OF THE FAIR-GROUNDS.

HE'S JUST WANDERING AROUND AIMLESSLY.

THEN IT'S NOT TOO LATE!

COME ON, NINJAS!

THE BOYS MAKE THEIR WAY TO THE AUCTION AREA WHERE PEOPLE ARE SHOWING OFF THEIR WARES.

ALL RIGHT, FOLKS, OUR NEXT ITEM UP FOR BIDS IS THIS LOVELY 19TH CENTURY LAMP.

AW DUDE CRAP. ALL OUR PARENTS ARE THERE.

PARK COUNTY COMMUNITY CENTER

EMERGENCY TOWN MEETING!

ENTRANCE

INSIDE THE COMMUNITY CENTER, THE ENTIRE TOWN HAS GATHERED, YOUNG AND OLD, AND EVERYONE IS SHOUTING AND YELLING.

ALRIGHT, PEOPLE, WE ARE ALL EXTREMELY UPSET OVER WHAT'S HAPPENED.

BUT LET'S TRY TO SPEAK ONE AT A TIME.

STAN AND KYLE ARE SITTING NEXT TO EACH OTHER, LOOKING SHEEPISHLY DOWN AT THE FLOOR AND THEN TO EACH OTHER.

WELL, LIKE THE REST OF YOU, I AM SHOCKED AND APPALLED AT WHAT HAPPENED!

I DON'T KNOW IF THE PARENTS ARE TO BLAME OR IF IT'S THE TIMES WE'RE LIVING IN, BUT SOMETHING HAS TO CHANGE!

67

BUTTERS

NOW GOSH DARN IT, LISTEN HERE!

JIMMY

WOW, WHAT A GREAT AUDIENCE.
I JUST FLEW INTO SOUTH PARK.
BOY, ARE MY CRUTCHES TIRED!

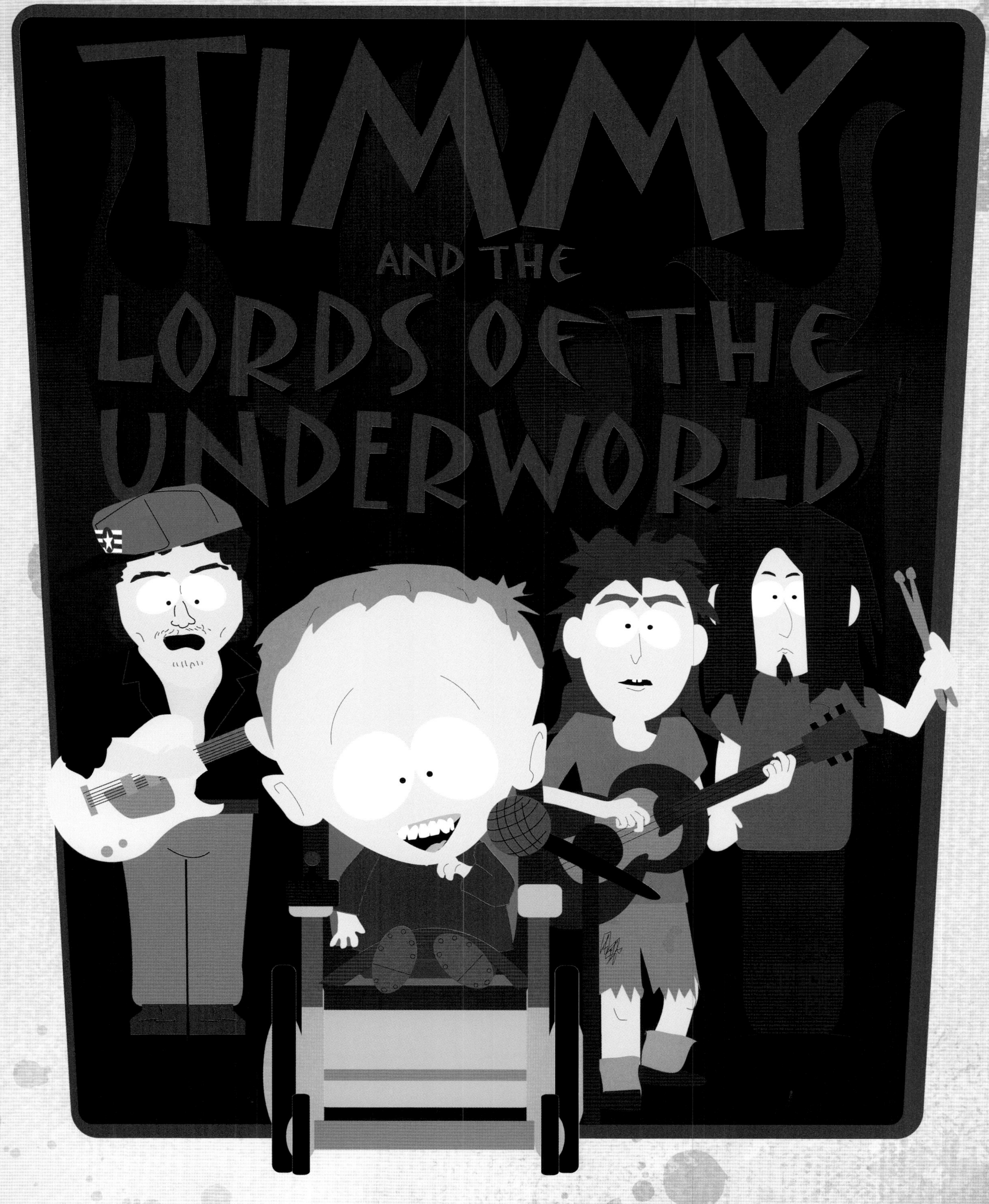
TIMMY
AND THE
LORDS OF THE
UNDERWORLD

TOWELIE

DON'T FORGET TO BRING A TOWEL!

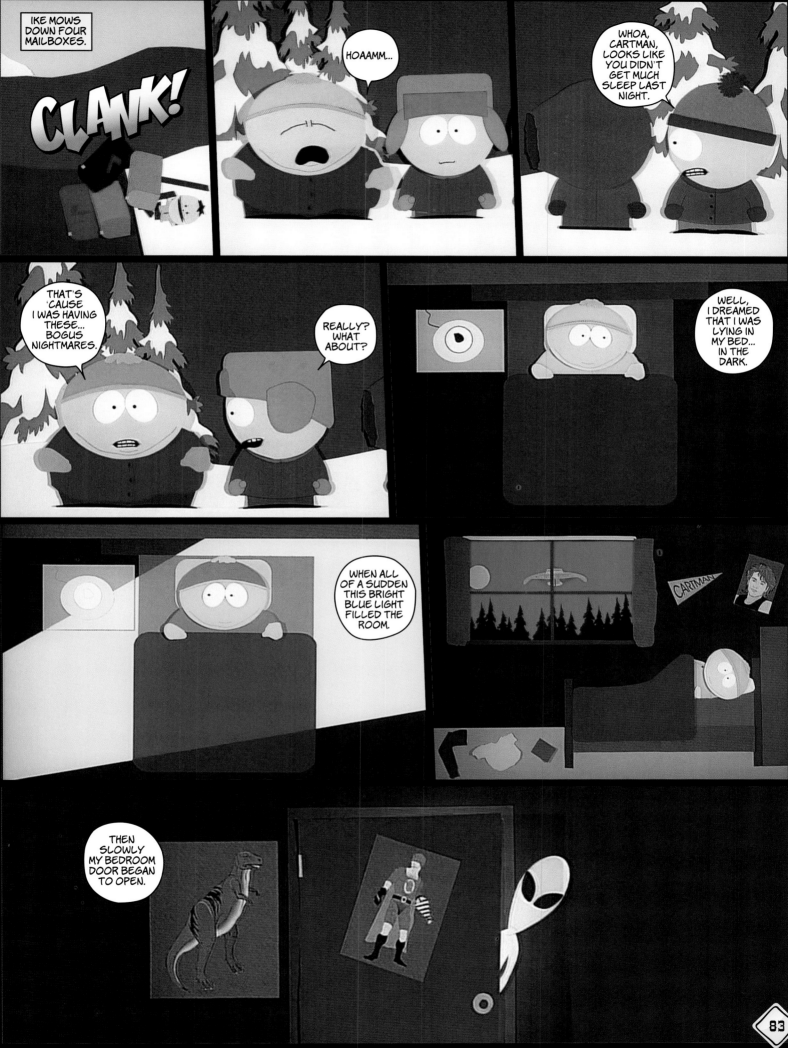

THE BOYS START GETTING ON.

SCHOOL BUS

STOP

WHY ARE YOU WALKIN' SO FUNNY CARTMAN?

SHUT UP!

THIS IS IT. THIS ONE'S FOR THE GAME.

KICK THE BABY!

PUNT

HAHA-HA.

SCHOOL BUS

CRASH

SCHOOL BUS

CRASH

IKE FLIES THROUGH THE FIRST WINDOW OF THE SCHOOL BUS AND CRASHES OUT THROUGH THE OTHER SIDE.

GOOD MORNING, MISS CRABTREE.

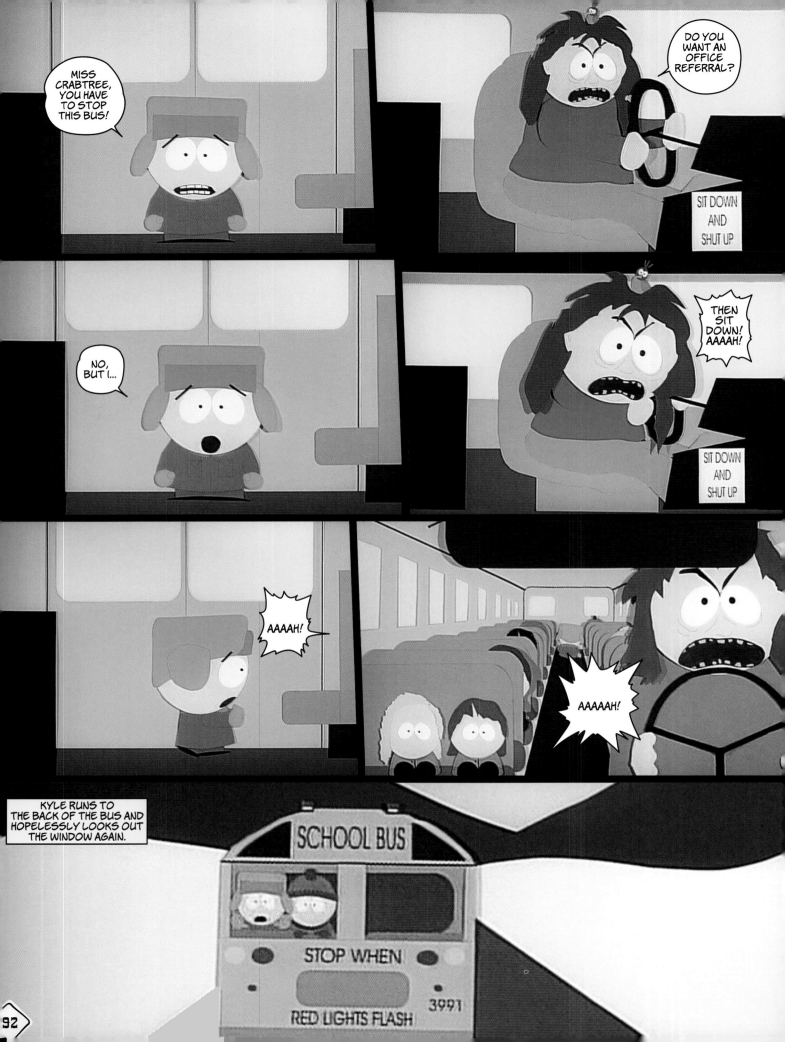

HAHAHA...

SOME-BODY'S BAKING BROWNIES.

THE ALIEN SHIP LEAVES THE PLANET.

VINK VINK

FARMER'S GRAZING FIELDS WITH A MUTILATED COW.

THAT'S THE THIRD COW THIS MONTH.

CATTLE RANCH

AT THIS RATE ALL OF MY CATTLE ARE GONNA DIE BEFORE THE WINTER'S THROUGH.

MOO

MOO

THE COWS LOOK UP WITH CONCERN.

THIS IS NOTHING OUT OF THE UN-USUAL. COWS TURN THEMSELVES INSIDE OUT ALL THE TIME.

THE COWS NOTICE SOMETHING.

MOOoo   MOOoo

ONE ALIEN WHISTLES.

FUU FUU

THE COWS START RUNNING AWAY FROM THEM.

CATTLE RANCH

MOO

MOOo

HEY! MY CATTLE!

MOOo   MOOo

YOU SEE, THERE IS SOMETHIN' FUNNY GOIN' ON!

THERE'S NOTHING FUNNY GOING ON. I'LL GET THOSE COWS BACK.

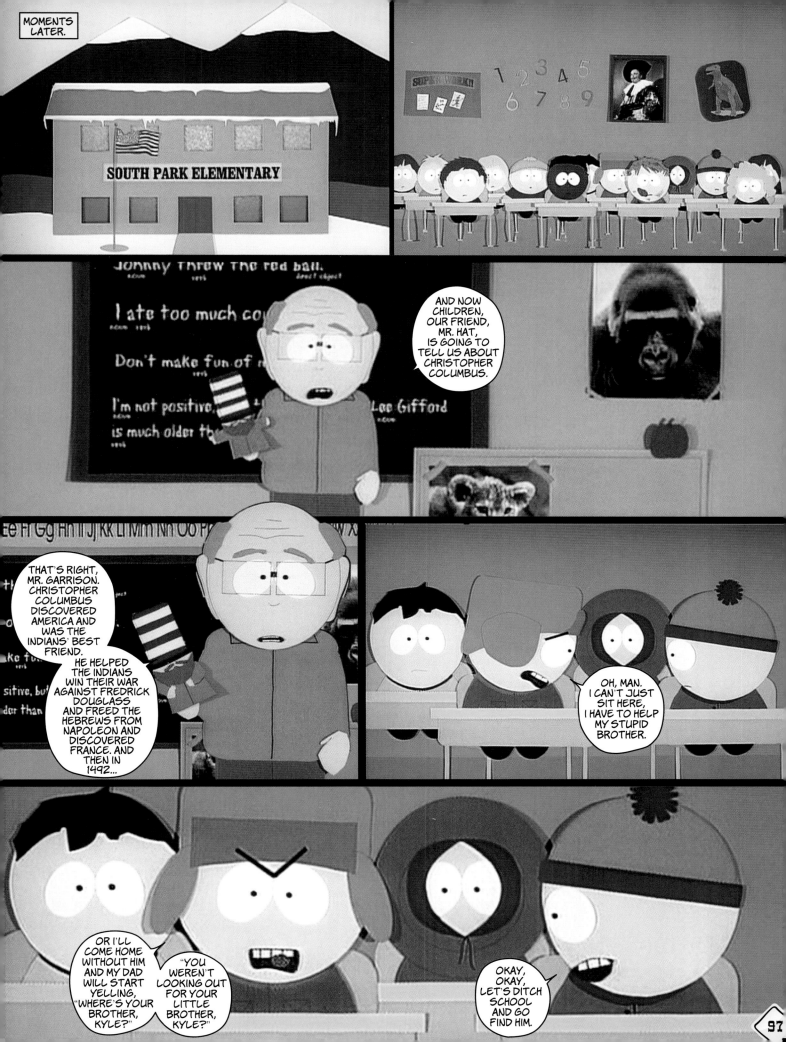

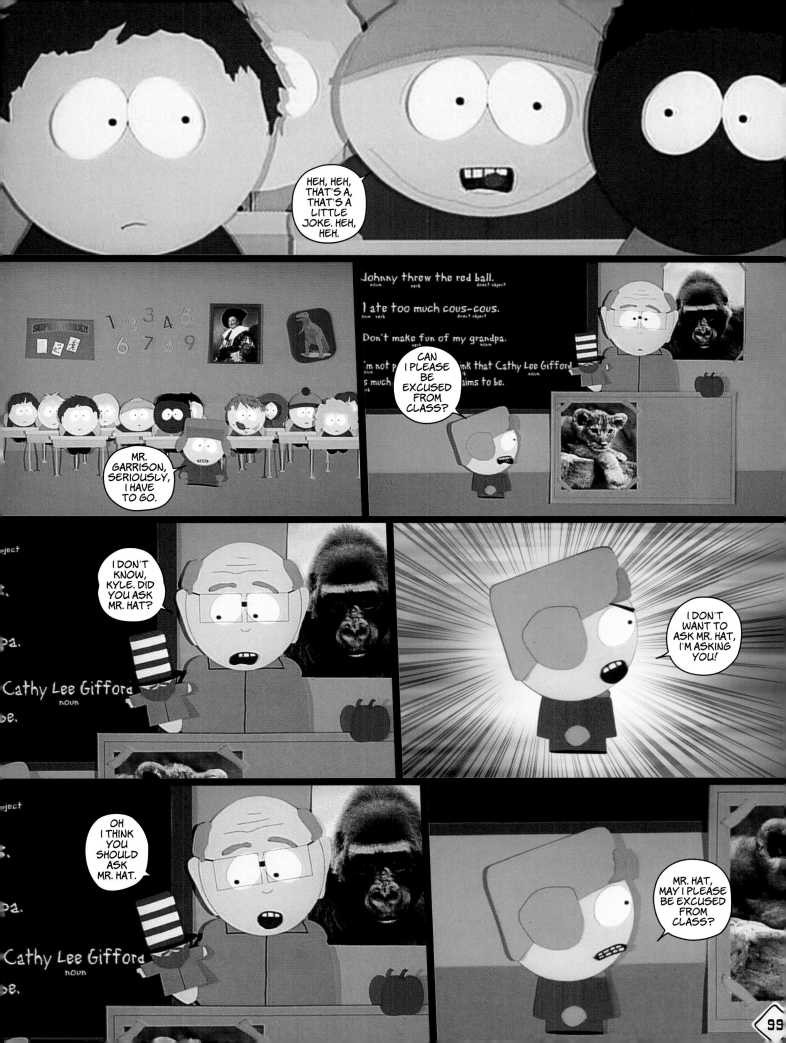

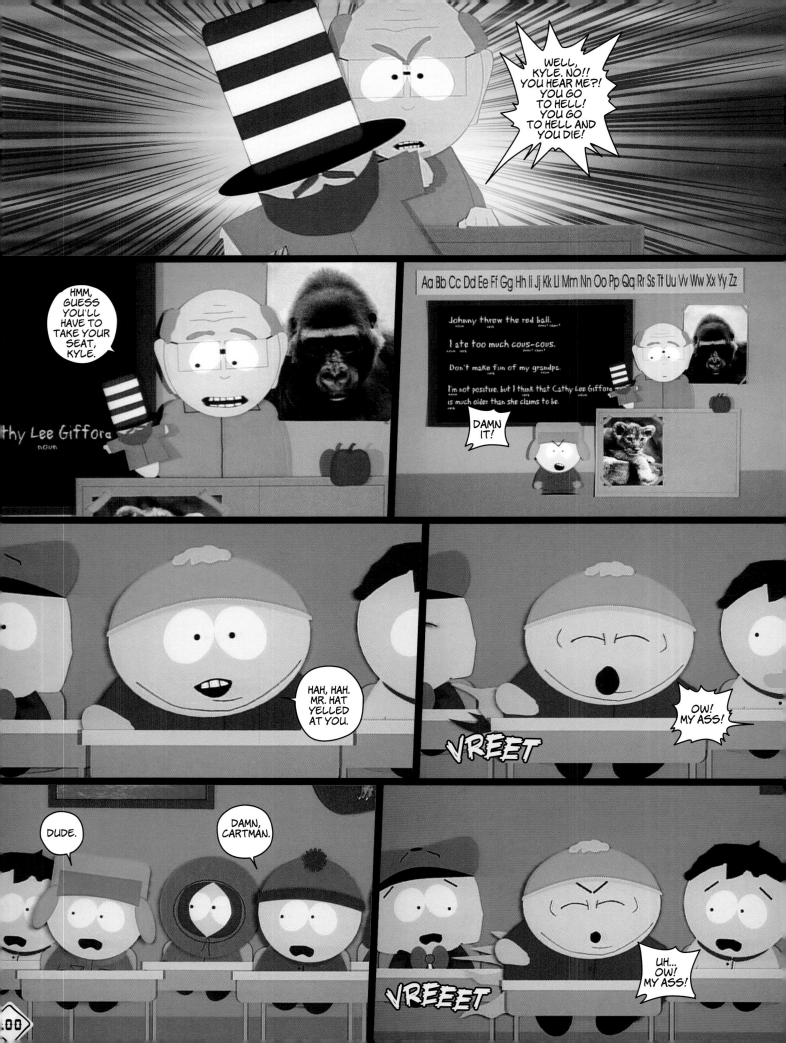

DUDE, HE'S FARTING FIRE.

IT'S THE ALIEN ANAL PROBE. IT'S SHOOTING FIRE FROM CARTMAN'S RECTUM.

NO, THAT WAS JUST A DREAM.

ERIC, DO YOU NEED TO SIT IN THE CORNER UNTIL YOUR FLAMING GAS IS UNDER CONTROL?

NO, MR. GARRISON, I'M FINE.

JUST THEN, CARTMAN FARTS A HUGE FIREBALL.

WHOAA...

VREET

101

AT THE TRAIN STATION. COWS FLOCK IN FROM ALL AROUND AND STAND IN LINE, WAITING TO BOARD THE TRAIN OUT OF TOWN.

NEXT TRAIN TO DENVER

DEPARTS 12:30

LINE FORMS HERE

HEY, YOU COWS CAN'T GET ON THIS TRAIN!

South Park Express

THIS IS A PEOPLE TRAIN. YOU COWS HAVE NO BUSINESS ON A PEOPLE TRAIN, ALL RIGHT? 'CAUSE YOU'RE COWS.

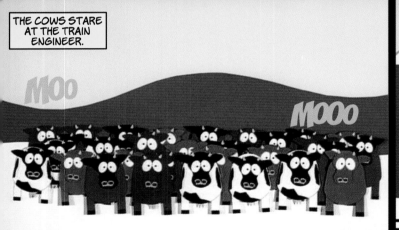

THE COWS STARE AT THE TRAIN ENGINEER.

MOO

MOOO

NO, NO, NO. DON'T TRY ANY OF THAT COW HYPNOSIS ON ME, ALL RIGHT? 'CAUSE IT'S NOT GONNA WORK.

South Park Express

OFFICER BARBRADY DRIVES BY WITH HIS LIGHTS FLASHING.

HOLD IT RIGHT THERE, COWS!

DING! DING!

SOUTH PARK

"To Patronize and Annoy"

2 TRACKS

COWS SPLIT UP AND RUN OFF MOOING.

MOOOO

MOOOO

102

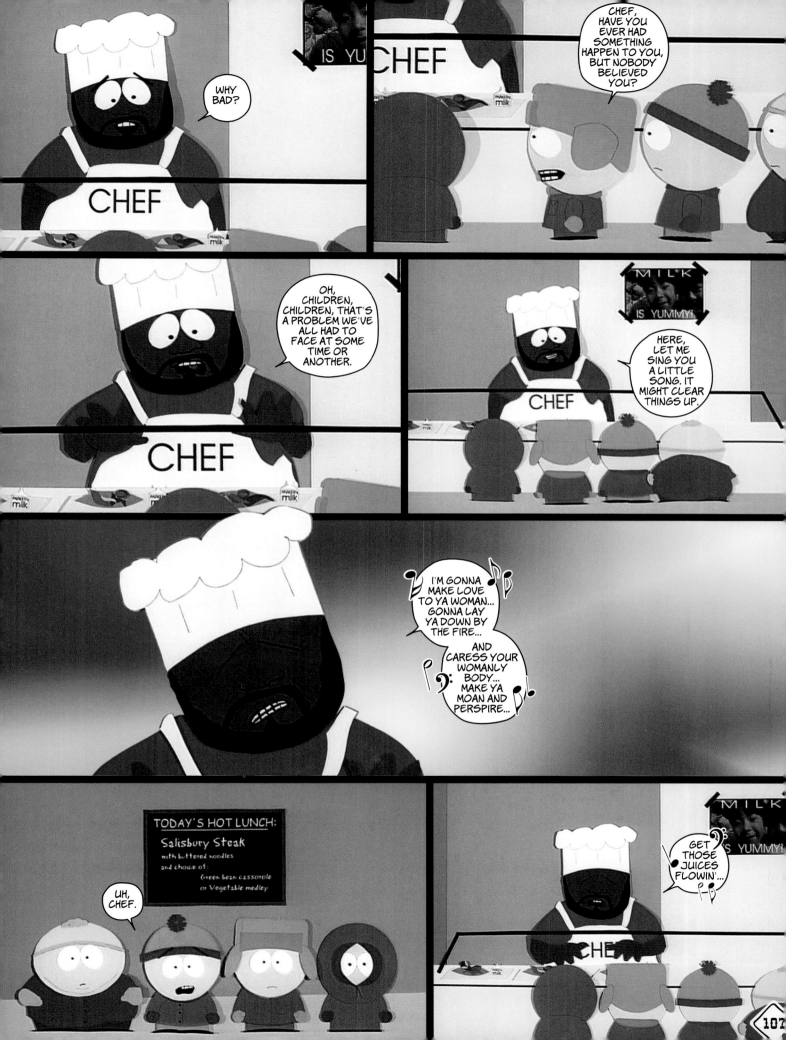

BINK BINK

WHOA!

WHAT?

THAT WAS COOL!

IT'S UH SOME KIND OF SYMBIOTIC, METAMOR-PHOSIS DEVICE.

THIS COULD MEAN THE VISITORS WANT TO COMMUNICATE WITH US.

OH, I SEE. NOW YOU'RE GOING TO JOIN IN ON THE LITTLE JOKE HUH?

IT'S NO JOKE, CHILDREN, THIS IS BIG!

PLEASE, CHEF, IF I DON'T GET OUT OF SCHOOL AND GET MY LITTLE BROTHER BACK FROM THE ALIENS.

MY PARENTS ARE GONNA DISOWN ME.

UUH, HOLD ON NOW, HOLD ON NOW.

YOU GUYS SURE ARE GOING A LONG WAY TO TRY AND SCARE ME. I WANT MY SALISBURY STEAK!

FIRE DRILL! FIRE DRILL! EVERYBODY OUT!

IN CASE OF FIRE PULL

BA-RING! BA-RING!

OKAY CHILDREN, THIS IS YOUR CHANCE!

KILLER! THANKS, CHEF.

THE BOYS LEAVE SCHOOL.

OH MAN, FIRST CONTACT WITH THE ALIEN VISITORS. I'VE GOT TO GET MYSELF READY.

CHEF

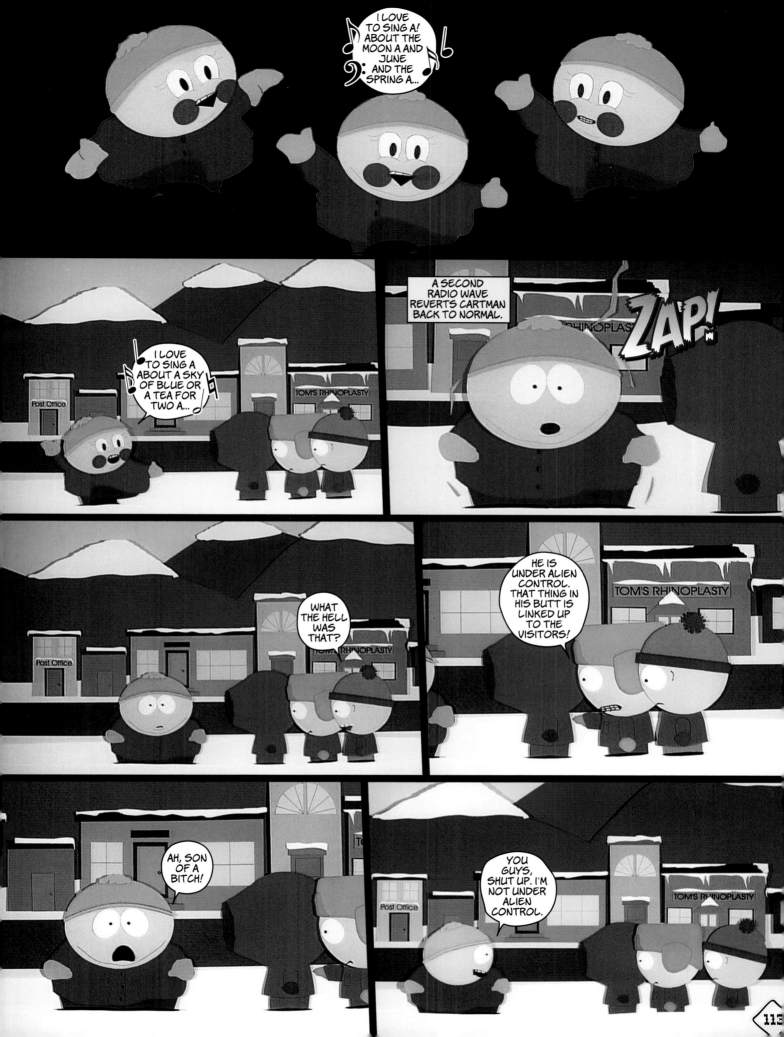

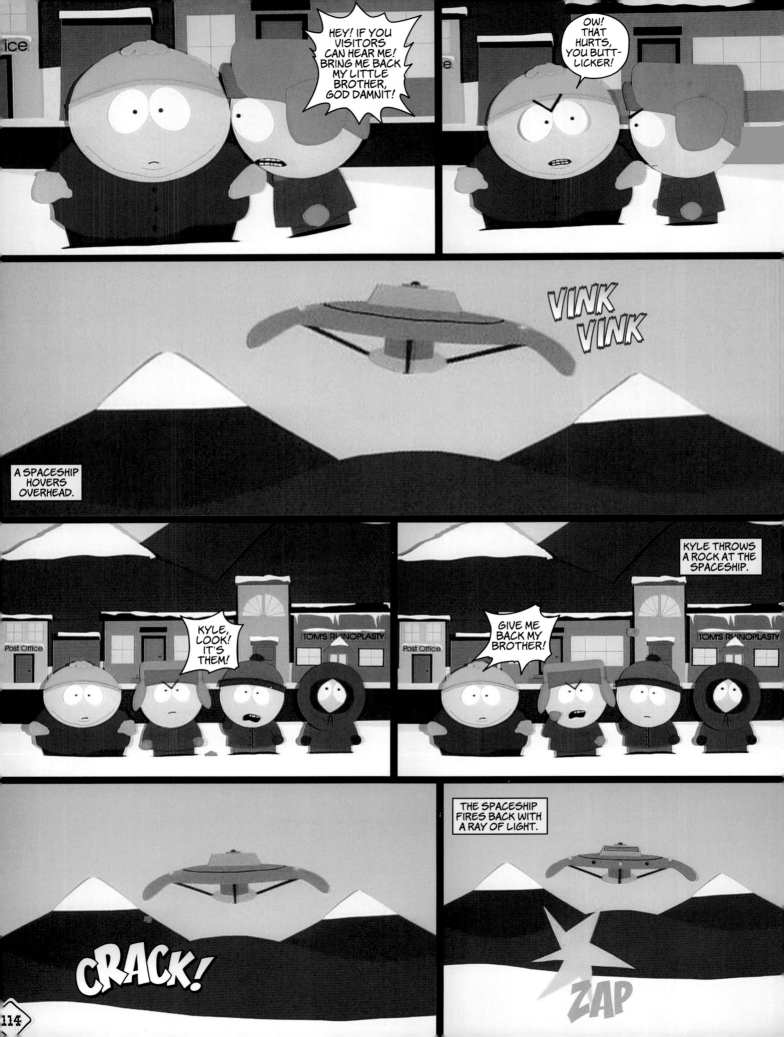

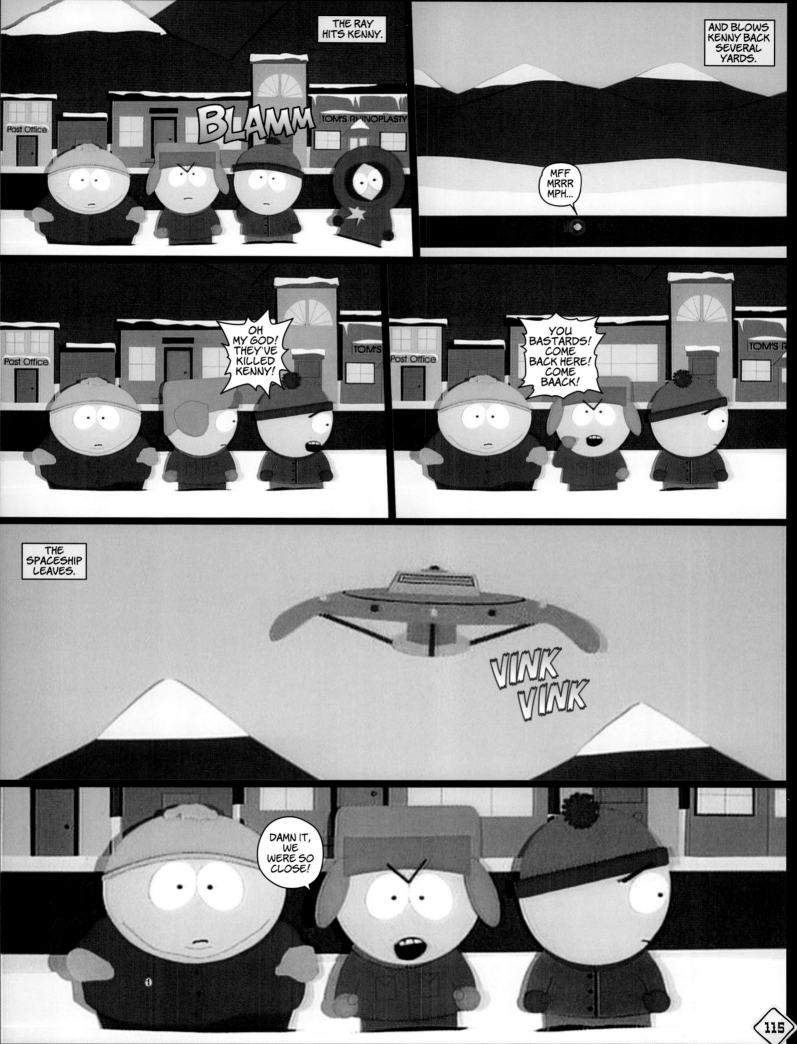

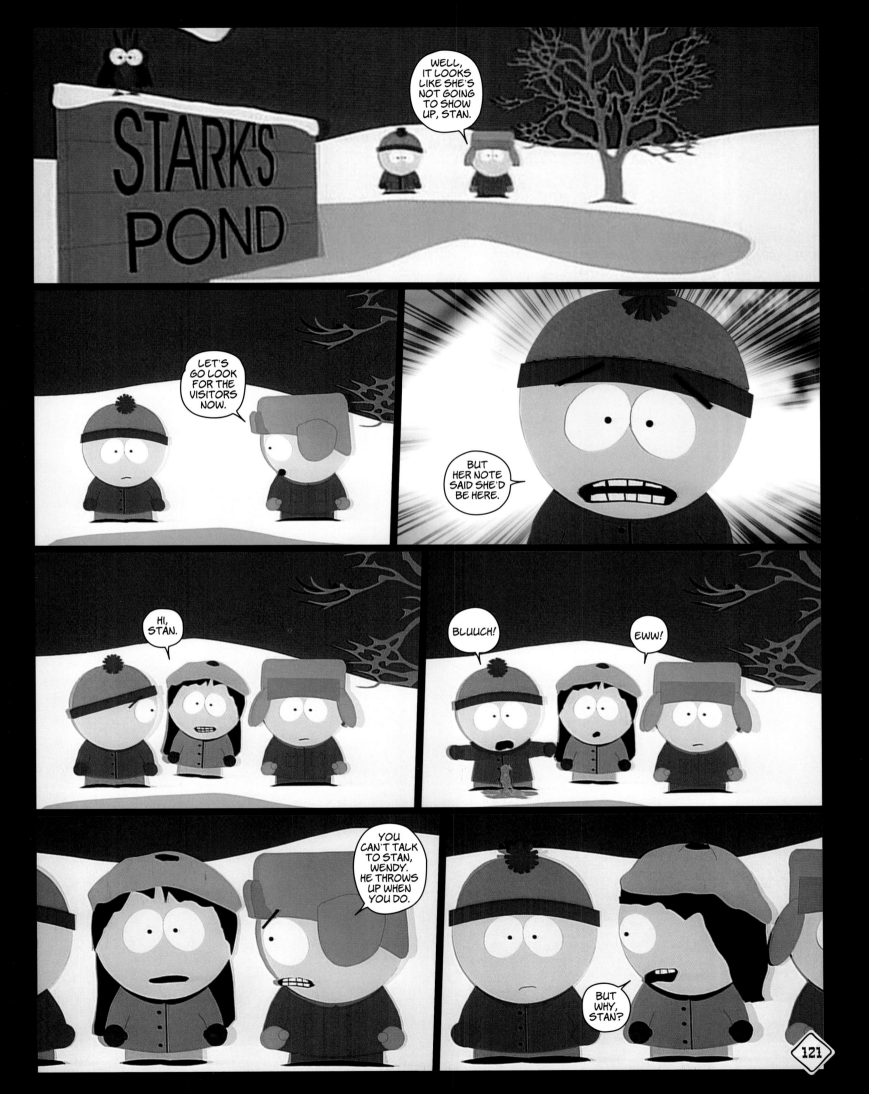

BLAA BA WAH WAHH.

IKE, JUMP DOWN, NOW! FOR THE LOVE OF GOD, IKE, JUMP!

BO HAM ME!

MOO MOO

MOO... MOO... MOO... MOO...

GREETINGS, COWS OF EARTH. WE COME IN PEACE.

MOO.OO

REALLY?

MOO MOO MOO MOO MOO...

WE HAVE EXPERIMENTED WITH ALL THE BEINGS OF EARTH, AND HAVE LEARNED THAT YOU ARE THE MOST INTELLIGENT AND WISE.

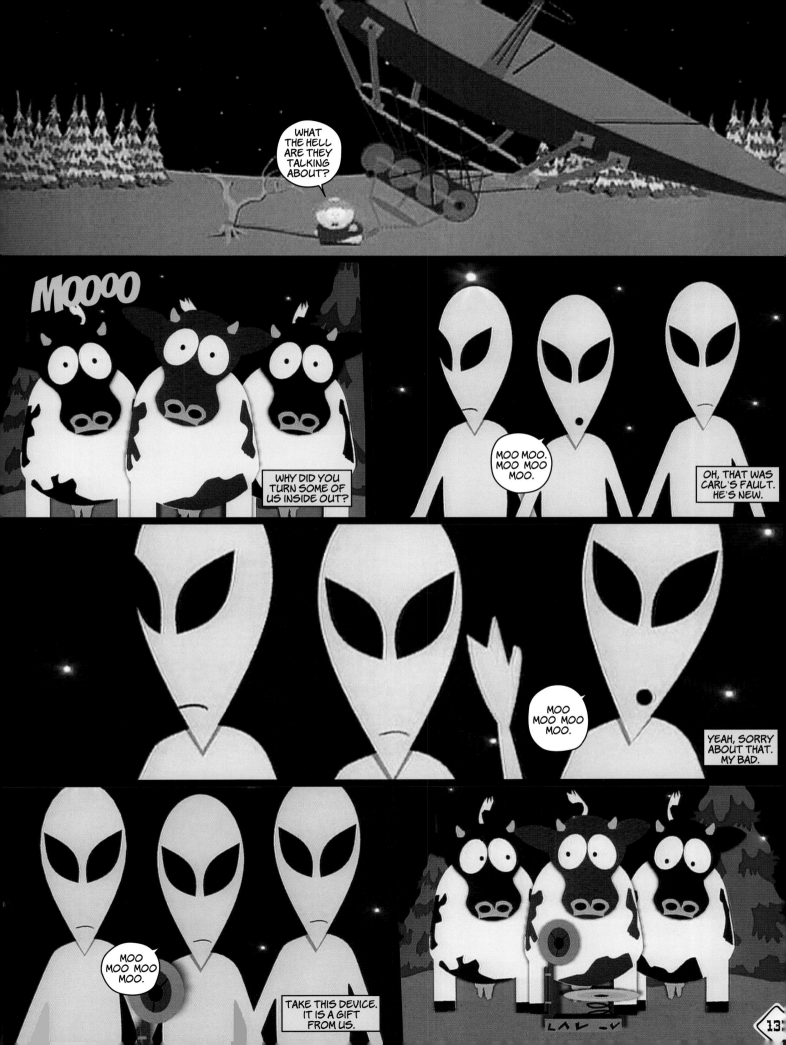

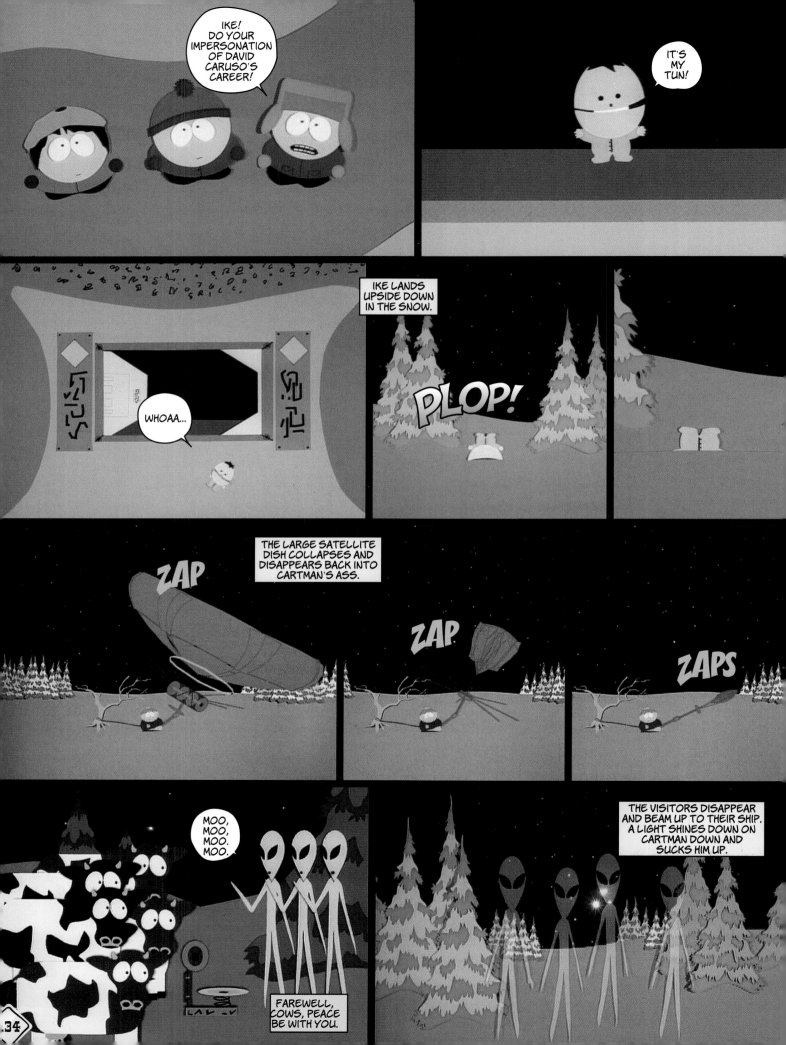

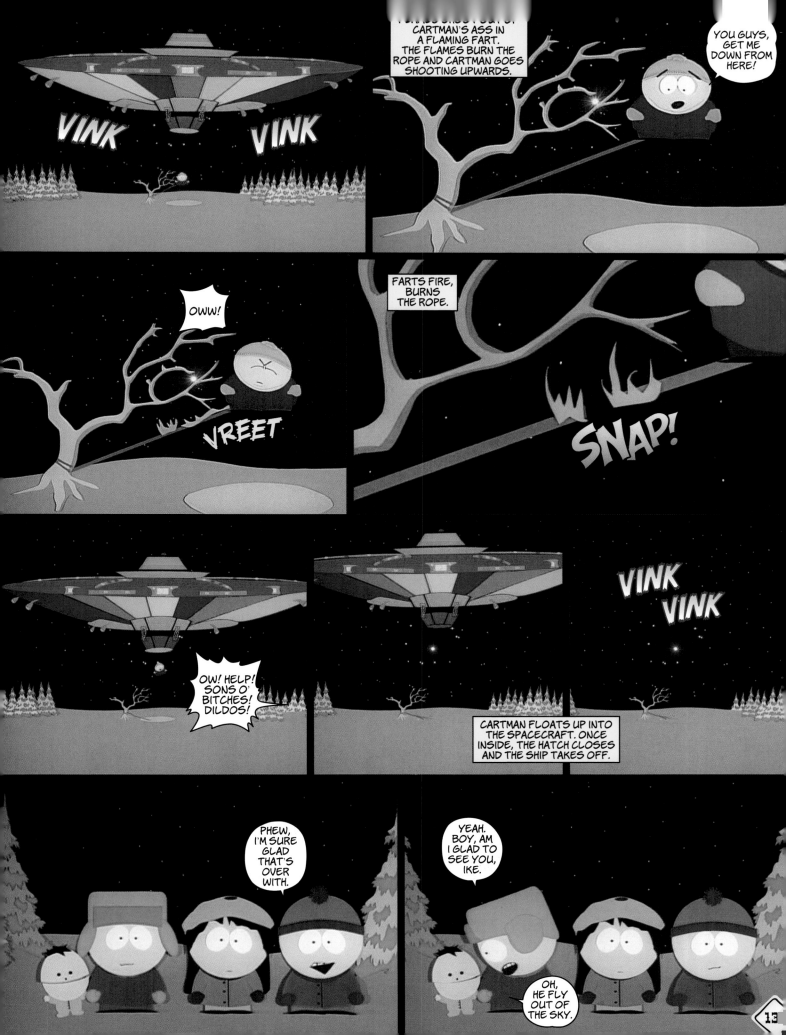

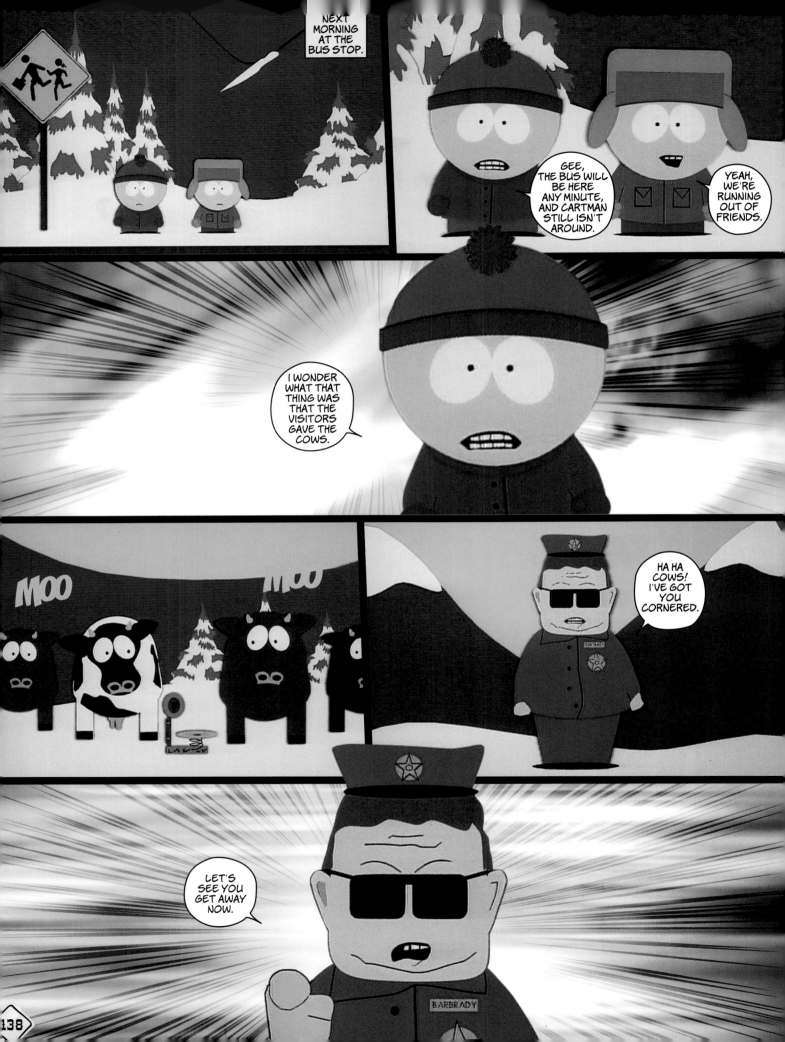

TONIGHT IS RIGHT FOR LOVE.